Third Edition

ACTIVITY MANUAL
ANSWER KEY

bju press®

Greenville, South Carolina

Note:
The fact that materials produced by other publishers may be referred to in this volume does not constitute an endorsement of the content or theological position of materials produced by such publishers. Any references and ancillary materials are listed as an aid to the student or the teacher and in an attempt to maintain the accepted academic standards of the publishing industry.

Activity Manual Answer Key
SCIENCE 2 Third Edition

Coordinating Author
Janet E. Snow

Contributing Author
Joyce Garland

Project Editor
Naomi Viola

Designer
Duane Nichols

Page Layout
Linda Hastie

Project Manager
Roxana P. Pérez

Consultants
Jamie Mellor
Charlotta Pace

Cover Design
Elly Kalagayan

Front Cover Illustration
Aaron Dickey

Back Cover Illustration
Matt Bjerk

Photo Acquisition
Rita Mitchell
LaDonna Ryggs
Brenda Hansen
Holly Nelson

Illustrators
Courtney Godbey
Lynda Slattery

Produced in cooperation with the Bob Jones University School of Education and Bob Jones Elementary School.

Photograph credits appear on page 145.

© 2010 BJU Press
Greenville, South Carolina 29614

Printed in the United States of America

ISBN 978-1-59166-965-4

15 14 13 12 11 10 9 8 7 6 5 4 3 2 1

Contents

Use your senses to describe the object your teacher gives you.

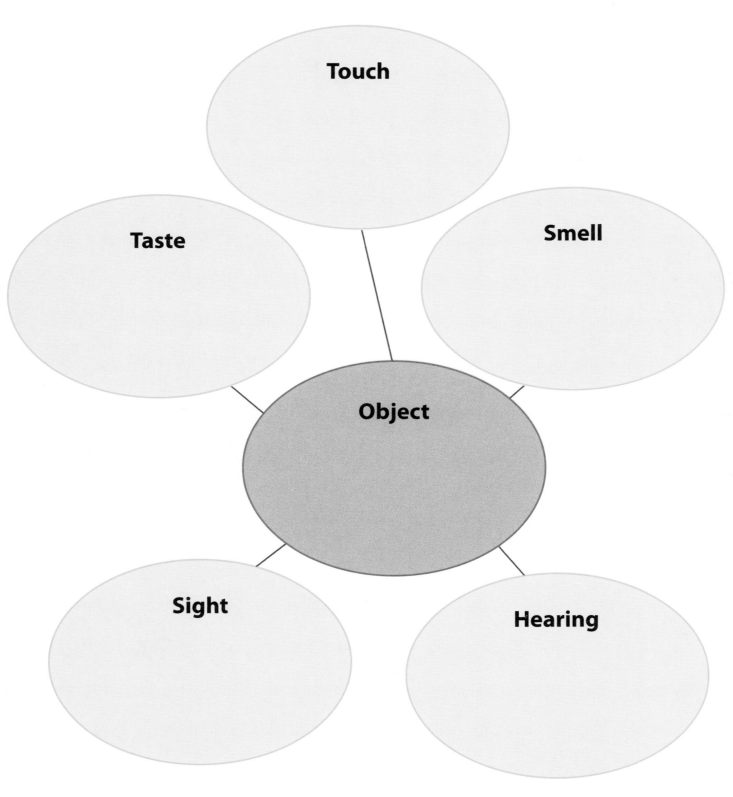

Touch

Taste

Smell

Object

Sight

Hearing

Put an *X* by the phrase that tells what will happen next.

_____ It is going to be a sunny day.

__X__ It is going to rain.

__X__ The towel will get dry.

_____ The towel will stay wet.

_____ The roller coaster will stay at the top of the track.

__X__ The roller coaster will roll to the bottom of the track.

Draw lines to match each tool with what it is used for.

1.

   used to measure how much space something takes up

2.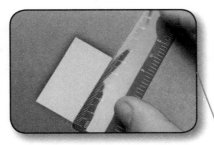

   used to measure how hot or cold something is

3.

   used to measure how much matter is in something

4.

   used to make things look bigger

5.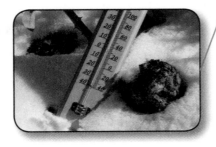

   used to measure how long something is

Keeping Cool

Name _____

Instructions for this activity are in the Teacher's Edition.

ACTIVITY

Problem

Does color affect temperature?

Materials

black paper
white paper
tape
2 thermometers

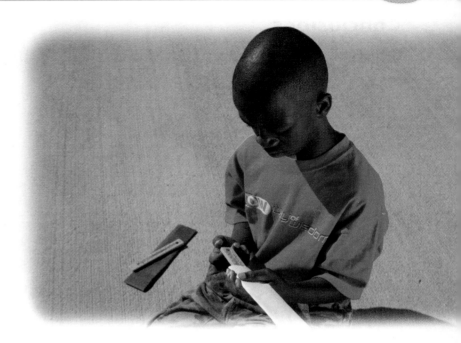

Hypothesis

The thermometer in black paper will change temperature

_____ than the thermometer in white paper.

(more / less)

Procedure

Complete the chart.

Temperature	Black Paper	White Paper
At the Beginning		
After an Hour		

Conclusions

1. Which thermometer had the most change in temperature?

   the one in the black paper

2. Was your hypothesis correct?

3. Based on your results from this activity, what color would make you warmer on a summer day?

   black

Name _____

A. Look at each picture. Circle the science process skill that is being used.

1.

communicating

(measuring)

2.

(observing)

classifying

3.

predicting

(classifying)

B. Number the steps of an experiment in order.

___3___ Plan and do your test.

___1___ Ask a question.

___5___ Communicate what you have learned.

___2___ Form a hypothesis.

___4___ Draw conclusions.

C. Circle the picture that answers the question. Explain your answer.

Joshua wants to find the answer to the question, "Will a toy car travel faster on wood or carpet?" Which picture shows a fair way to test that question?

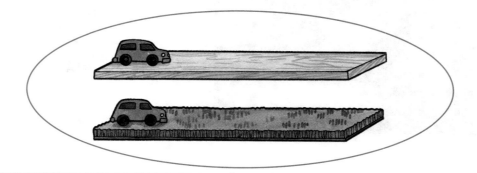

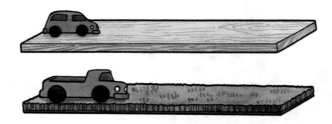

Why is the other way not a fair test?

The toy cars are not the same.

Is It Alive?

Student Text pages 16–19

Name _____

A. Color the things that are living. Do not color the things that are not alive.

Color

Color

Color

Color

B. Answer the question.

What are three things that all living things need?

air, food, and water

What Seeds Need

Name _____

ACTIVITY

Problem

Does a seed need water to grow?

Materials

2 resealable plastic bags
2 paper towels
water
spray bottle
4 seeds

Hypothesis

The seeds in the bag _____ water will grow.
(with / without)

Procedure

A. Complete the chart.

	Water	No Water
Date Seeds Were Put in Bag		
Date Seeds Began to Grow		

B. Draw a picture of what the seeds that are growing look like.

Science 2
Activity Manual

Conclusions

1. What was the only difference between the bags of seeds?
   One bag had water, and one did not.

2. Which seeds grew?
   the ones with water

3. What can you learn about living things from this activity?
   Living things need water to grow.

Name _____

A. Draw lines to match each young living thing with the correct adult.

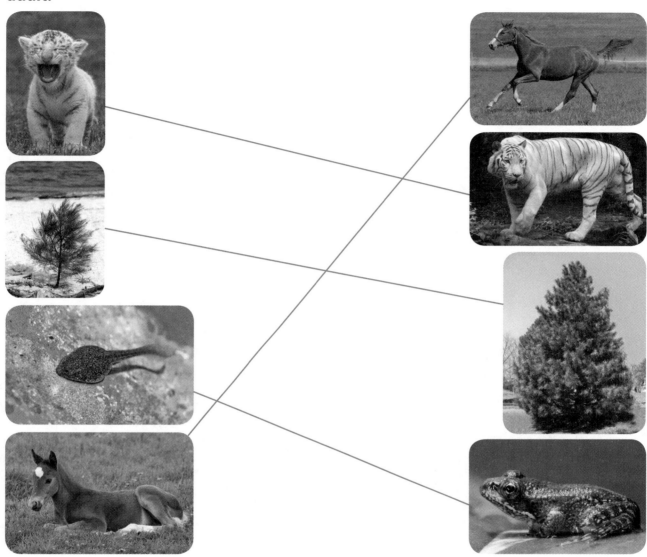

B. Answer the questions.

1. Do all babies look like their parents when they are born?

   no

2. Which young living thing in part A does not look like the adult?

   the tadpole

A. Cut out the butterfly wings. Keep each tab connected to its wing.

B. Follow the directions your teacher gives you.

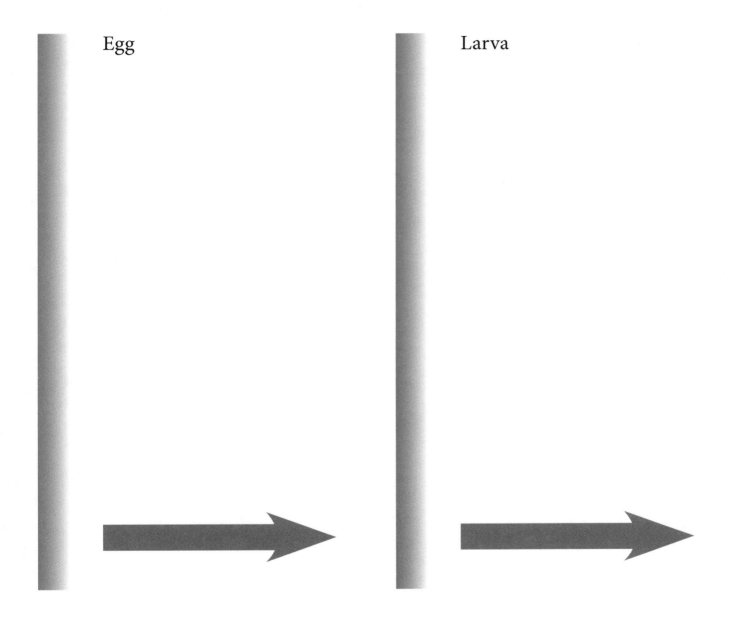

Egg

Larva

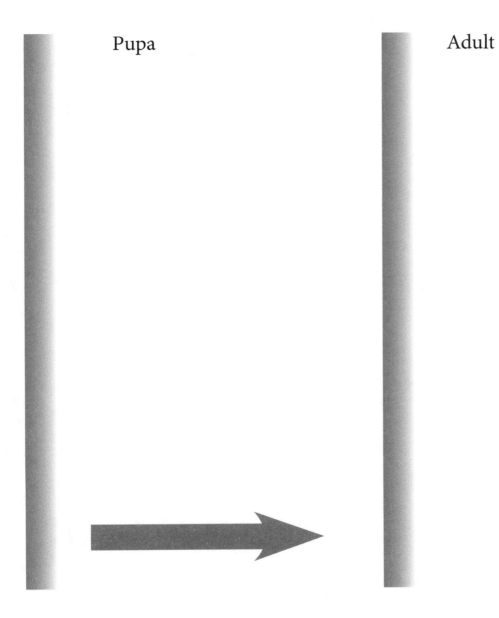

Pupa

Adult

Activity Manual

A. Fill in the blanks.

| change | food | grow | more | shelter | water |

1. Living things need

_____ *food* _____, air,

and _____ *water* _____.

2. Living things

_____ *grow* _____

and _____ *change* _____.

3. Living things need space and

_____ *shelter* _____.

4. Living things make _____

_____ *more* _____

living things.

B. Label the pictures.

Frog Life Cycle

adult
egg
tadpole

5. _egg_

6. _tadpole_

7. _adult_

Butterfly Life Cycle

adult
egg
larva
pupa

8. _egg_

9. _larva_

10. _pupa_

11. _adult_

Lesson 15; pp. 14–31
Chapter Review

Needing Light

Student Text pages 34–35

Name _____

Becka wants to plant some flowers in her yard. Help her decide where to plant each kind of flower.

Read the description of each flower. Write the letter of the garden spot that will best meet that plant's needs.

_C_ 1. Primrose
   This flowering plant grows low to the ground. It grows best when it gets both sun and shade throughout the day.

_B_ 2. Shasta daisy
   This tall, white flower likes to grow in sunny spots.

_A_ 3. Lily of the valley
   This plant has white, bell-shaped flowers. It can grow in very shady areas.

Science 2
Activity Manual

Growing Healthy
Student Text pages 36–37

Name _____

Problem
Do seeds need soil to grow into healthy plants?

Materials
2 clear plastic cups, 9 oz
paper towels
2 bean seeds
potting soil
water
metric measuring cup

Hypothesis

_____

Bean seeds _____ need soil to grow into healthy plants.
          (do / do not)

Procedure

A. Record the date each seed sprouts.

Paper Towels: _____   Soil: _____

B. Record your observations for each plant after the seed has sprouted.

Day	Paper Towels	Soil
1		
2		

Activity Manual

Day	Paper Towels	Soil
3		
4		
5		
6		

Conclusions

1. Which young plant was healthier?

   the one in the soil

2. Did the bean seeds need the soil to help them grow strong and healthy?

   yes

Name _____

A. Complete the matching section.

___A___ 1. make seeds

___C___ 2. hold the plant in the ground and take in water

___B___ 3. make food for the plant

___D___ 4. move water and food around the plant

A. flowers
B. leaves
C. roots
D. stems

B. Mark all the correct answers.

5. A plant needs

● air   ○ rocks

○ animals   ● soil

○ hot temperatures   ● space

● light   ● water

Different Seeds
Student Text pages 40–43

Name _____

Draw a line to match each kind of seed and plant.

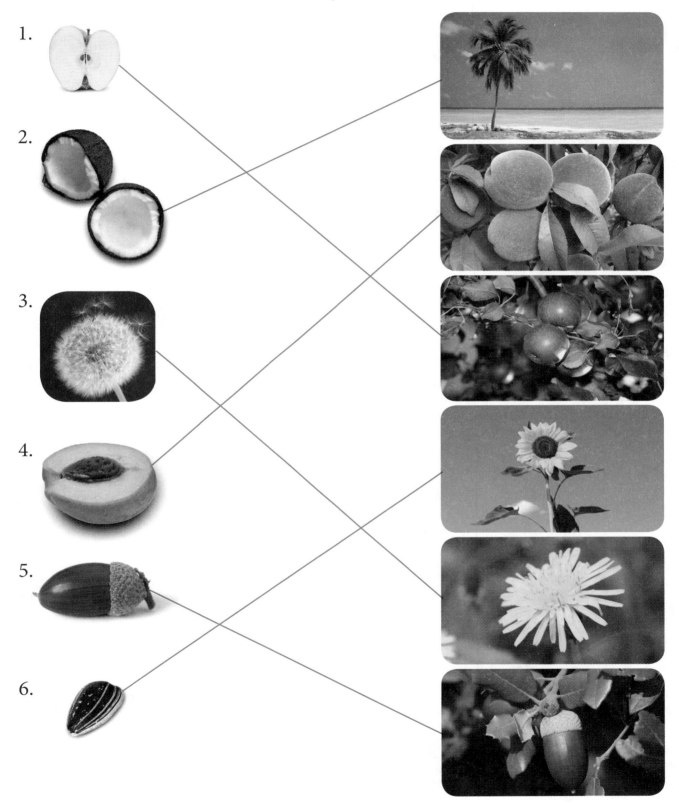

1.

2.

3.

4.

5.

6.

Color the pictures. Label each picture.

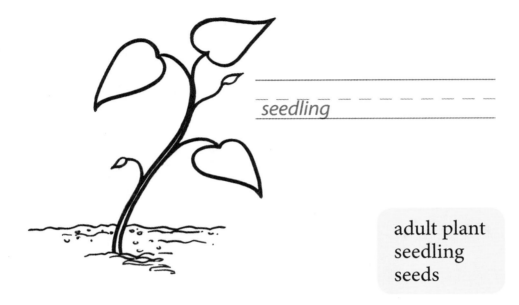

_____

seedling

adult plant
seedling
seeds

_____

adult plant

_____

seeds

A. Put an *X* by the correct answer.

1. Which part of a plant holds the plant in the ground?

   _____ leaves   _____ stems   __X__ roots

2. Which part of a plant makes food?

   __X__ leaves   _____ stems   _____ roots

3. Which part of a plant moves food and water?

   _____ flowers   __X__ stems   _____ roots

4. Which part of a plant makes seeds?

   _____ stems   _____ leaves   __X__ flowers

5. What is the outside covering of a seed called?

   _____ stored food   __X__ seed coat   _____ tiny plant

B. Answer the questions.

6. What is a young plant called?

   a seedling

7. What are three things plants need to grow?

   Possible answers: light, air, water, soil, space

8. What are two things that can scatter seeds?

   Possible answers: wind, water, animals

In the Neighborhood

Name _____

Use the picture to answer the questions.

1. There are seven mice in the picture. Are these mice a population or a habitat?

   a population

2. A bird is living in the tree. Is the tree a habitat or a community for the bird?

   a habitat

3. There is soil in this meadow. Is the soil part of the community or part of the environment?

   the environment

Different Environments
Student Text pages 52–55

Name _____

A. Decide whether the environment is a wet one or a dry one.
   Write *wet* or *dry* under each picture.

desert	tundra	rainforest

1. *dry*

2. *dry*

3. *wet*

B. Answer the questions.

4. Why do many desert plants need to be able to store water?

   It does not rain much in a desert.

5. Some tundra animals have fur that changes color when the seasons change. How does this help the animals?

   The color changes help the animals hide from other animals.

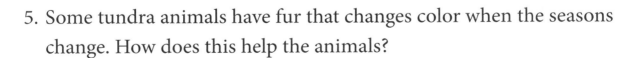

A. Fill in the blanks.

community	environment	habitat	population

1. All the living things in an area make up a _community_.

2. All the living things of one kind in an area make up a _population_.

3. Everything that surrounds a living thing is called its _environment_.

4. Where a plant or animal lives is called its _habitat_.

B. Write the letter of the correct answer.

__B__ 5. Which environment has many trees and bushes?
   A. the tundra   B. the woodland forest   C. the desert

__A__ 6. Which environment is very wet and has tall trees?
   A. the rainforest   B. the desert   C. the tundra

__C__ 7. Which environment is very dry?
   A. the rainforest   B. the woodland forest   C. the desert

__A__ 8. Which environment is very cold and dry?
   A. the tundra   B. the desert   C. the rainforest

C. Draw lines to match each environment with an animal that lives there.

9.

desert

10.

rainforest

11.

woodland forest

12.

tundra

Lesson 25; pp. 48–57
Review

Science 2
Activity Manual

Use your textbook and other resources to find information about the habitat you chose. Write your answers in the chart.

_____ (habitat)
What it is like:
Two animals that live there:
One plant that lives there:
Something interesting about this habitat:
Where this kind of habitat is found:
What you might use to build your model:

Checkup Time

Name _____

A. Mark the circle of the correct answer.

● True   1. All the living things of one kind in an area make
○ False   up a population.

○ True   2. A community is made up of only nonliving
● False   things.

● True   3. A habitat is where a living thing can find food,
○ False   water, and shelter.

● True   4. An environment is everything that surrounds a
○ False   living thing.

B. Draw lines to complete the matching section.

5. desert   a very wet land environment

6. ocean   a very dry environment

7. pond   a cold and dry environment

8. rainforest   a saltwater environment

9. tundra   an environment with many trees and bushes

10. woodland forest   a freshwater environment

C. Write the name of the environment where you are most likely to find each animal or plant.

desert   ocean   pond   rainforest   tundra   woodland forest

11. A cactus stores water to use later.

desert

12. A monkey eats fruit from tall trees.

rainforest

13. A duck has webbed feet for swimming.

pond

14. The Arctic fox has winter fur that blends in with its environment.

tundra

15. A deer hides in the bushes of its environment.

woodland forest

16. Colorful fish live in the coral reef of this environment.

ocean

Lesson 28; pp. 46–63
Chapter Review

Science 2
Activity Manual

What's the Difference?
Student Text pages 66–69

Name _____

Complete the chart.

by chance	many times
during the Flood	over millions of years
flood	perfect
God spoke	slowly

Creation	Evolution
God spoke and made the earth.	The earth was made _by chance_ .
God made the earth _perfect_ . The earth changed after Adam and Eve sinned.	The earth changed _many times_ .
Man's sin caused God to send a _flood_ that covered the whole earth.	The changes were made _slowly_ over a very long time.
Most fossils probably formed _during the Flood_ _____ .	Fossils formed _over millions of years_ _____ .

Circle *T* if the sentence is true. Circle *F* if the sentence is false.
Follow the directions in the chart to color the puzzle.

1.	Rocks and fossils give clues about the earth's past.	(T) F	If true, color every 7. If false, color every 5.
2.	Evolution and Creation are two different beliefs.	(T) F	If true, color every 1. If false, color every 8.
3.	Fossils are parts of living things preserved by nature.	(T) F	If true, color every 10. If false, color every 2.
4.	Fossils formed over millions of years.	T (F)	If true, color every 4. If false, color every 12.
5.	Most fossils formed during the Flood.	(T) F	If true, color every 6. If false, color every 3.
6.	Fossils are found in only a few places.	T (F)	If true, color every 11. If false, color every 9.

A large fossil of a _____*cockroach*_____ was found in an Ohio

coal mine. Many other fossils have also been found in the mine.

Activity Manual

A. Fill in the blanks.

cast   Creation   evolution   Flood   fossil   mold

1. Any part of a living thing preserved by nature is called a
   _____ *fossil* _____.

2. Most fossils probably formed during the _____ *Flood* _____.

3. A person who believes in _____ *Creation* _____ believes that
   God made all things.

4. A person who believes in _____ *evolution* _____ believes that the
   earth was made by chance.

5. Sometimes mud hardens around a living thing that died. The hole that
   is left is called a _____ *mold* _____.

6. A mold that fills with mud and hardens is called a
   _____ *cast* _____. It is a copy of the living thing.

B. Mark the circles of all the true sentences. Do not mark the circle beside any sentence that is false.

● 7. Fossils form when living things are quickly buried by mud or sand.

● 8. Fossils are found all over the earth.

○ 9. Petrified fossils are animals that froze in ice or snow.

● 10. Some fossils are found in amber, a type of tree sap that is preserved.

● 11. Marks made by living things can become fossils.

○ 12. Fossils can form in only one way.

Dinosaurs

Name _____

Sir Richard Owen was an English scientist who found some fossils that he wanted to describe. He put together the word *dinosaur* and began using it in 1841. Then other scientists began using the word *dinosaur* to describe certain kinds of fossils.

The Bible was translated into English hundreds of years earlier. So the word *dinosaur* is not in our Bibles. However, there are some Bible verses that might be talking about these same animals.

Read Job 40:15–24. Then use your Bible to answer the questions.

1. What is this animal's name? (v. 15) _____ *behemoth* _____

2. Whom did God make at the same time as He made this animal? (v. 15) _____ *man/people* _____

3. What does this animal eat? (v. 15) _____ *grass, plants* _____

4. What is this animal's tail like? (v. 17) _____ *a cedar* _____

5. What metal are this animal's bones like? (v. 18) _____ *brass/bronze, iron* _____

No known animal living now fits this description. We can tell from the way Job describes this animal that it was very big and had a large tail. It might have been a dinosaur!

A. Fill in the blanks.

all over	Creation	evolution	Flood	fossils	mud

1. A person who believes in _____*Creation*_____ believes that God made all things.

2. A person who believes in _____*evolution*_____ believes that the earth was made by chance and changed many times.

3. _____*Fossils*_____ are parts of living things preserved by nature.

4. Fossils form when living things are quickly buried by _____*mud*_____ or sand.

5. Most fossils were probably formed during the _____*Flood*_____.

6. Fossils are found _____*all over*_____ the earth.

B. Color the dinosaur green if the answer is true. Color it brown if the answer is false.

7. A dinosaur is an animal that lived long ago.

green

8. *Extinct* means that a certain kind of animal is still alive.

brown

9. The *Tyrannosaurus rex* was a small dinosaur that walked on all four legs.

brown

10. Some dinosaurs were very small.

green

11. Some dinosaurs laid eggs.

green

C. Answer the questions.

12. What are three different kinds of fossils?

Possible answers: petrified fossils, a mold, a cast, amber, frozen fossils

13. What kind of dinosaur had a row of bones along its back?

a Stegosaurus

Lesson 34; pp. 64–77
Chapter Review

Science 2
Activity Manual

Label the places on the globe.

continent   island   ocean

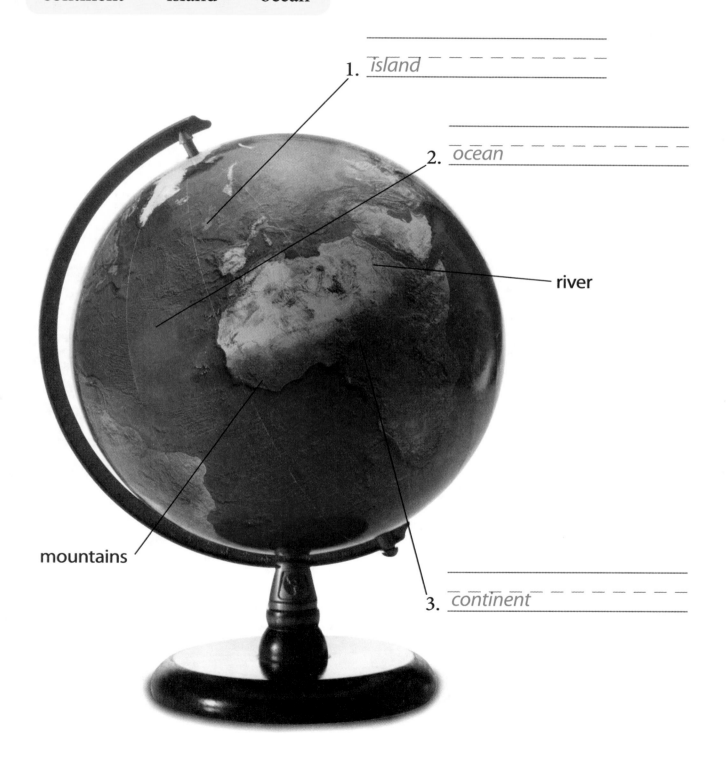

1. _island_ _____

2. _ocean_ _____

river

mountains

3. _continent_ _____

Checkup Time

Student Text pages 80–87

Name _____

Complete the puzzle.

Across

2. Large areas of water are called _____.

4. Large areas of land are called _____.

7. An opening in the earth's surface that allows hot, melted rock to flow out is a _____.

Down

1. An _____ happens when large areas of the earth's surface move.

3. Most of the earth is covered by _____.

5. Small areas of land in the middle of water are called _____.

6. A _____ is a model of the earth.

A. Color the layers of the earth. Use the color key.

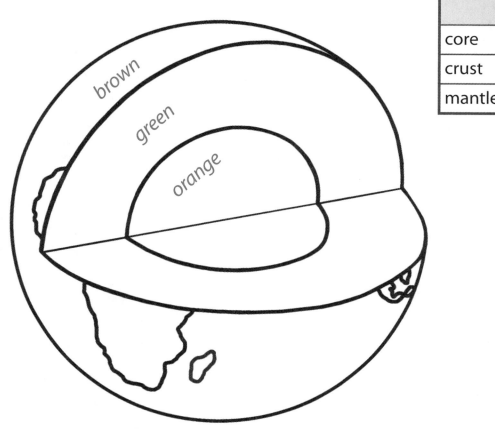

Key	
core	
crust	
mantle	

B. Answer the questions.

1. Is the mantle thinner or thicker than the crust?

   thicker

2. What is the mantle made of?

   hot, melted rock

3. What is the center of the earth called?

   the core

The Earth's Layers
Student Text pages 90–91

Name _____

ACTIVITY

Purpose
Make a model of the layers of the earth.

Materials
3 colors of clay (red, blue, and green)
ruler
piece of thread
crayons or colored pencils

Procedure
Draw and color the layers you see after you cut the ball apart. Label the layers of the earth.

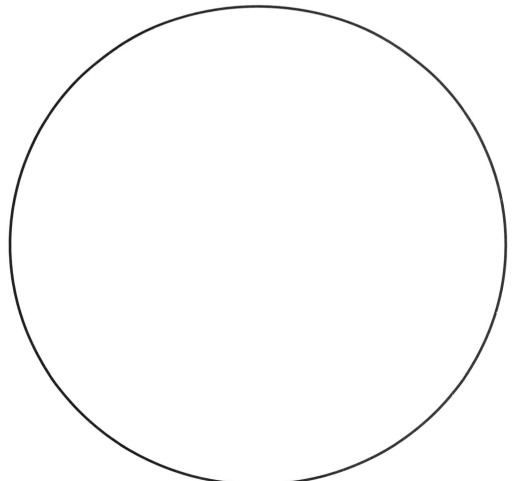

Science 2
Activity Manual

Conclusions

1. Which layer of the earth is the thinnest?

   the crust

2. Which layer of the earth is in the center?

   the core

A. Mark the circle of the correct answer.

1. A globe is a model of the _____.

   ● earth   ○ sky

2. Most of the earth's surface is covered by _____.

   ○ land   ● water

3. Large areas of water are called _____.

   ● oceans   ○ continents

4. Large areas of land are called _____.

   ○ oceans   ● continents

5. A crack in the earth's surface that allows hot, melted rock to flow out is called _____.

   ○ an earthquake   ● a volcano

6. The _____ is the layer of the earth that is made of hot, melted rock.

   ○ crust   ● mantle

7. When hot, melted rock comes out of the earth, it is called _____.

   ● lava   ○ an ocean

B. Answer the questions.

8. What happens when large areas of the earth's surface move suddenly?

   an earthquake

9. What are the three layers of the earth?

   the crust, mantle, and core

10. How do scientists infer what is inside the earth?

    They look at what happens on the surface of the earth.

Complete the puzzle. Fill in the shaded column for number 7.

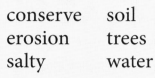

conserve	soil
erosion	trees
salty	water

```
        N
1. _W_ _A_ _T_ _E_ _R_
        T
        U
2. _T_ _R_ _E_ _E_ _S_
        A
3. _S_ _A_ _L_ _T_ _Y_
        R
        E
        S
        O
        U
4. _E_ _R_ _O_ _S_ _I_ _O_ _N_
5. _C_ _O_ _N_ _S_ _E_ _R_ _V_ _E_
        E
6. _S_ _O_ _I_ _L_
```

1. a natural resource that is a basic need of all living things

2. a natural resource that takes years to grow

3. describes most of the earth's water

4. what we call soil's movement from one place to another on the earth's surface

5. means to not waste or to use something wisely

6. a natural resource that helps plants grow

7. things in nature that God has given us to use

Draw a picture that shows each resource.

Water	**Soil**
Trees	**Fossil Fuels**

Checkup Time

Name _____

A. Circle the things that are natural resources.

B. Answer the questions.

1. Which natural resource comes from living things that died and were crushed?

   fossil fuels

2. What are three kinds of fossil fuels?

   oil, coal, and natural gas

3. What problem can fossil fuels sometimes cause?

   pollution

A. Draw lines to complete the matching section.

1. reduce   to use something again

2. reuse   to make something new out of an object

3. recycle   to use less of something

B. Answer the questions. *Answers will vary. Some answers are suggested for each question if you need to help the student think of ideas.*

4. Your little sister has an old plastic wading pool. What are two other ways you could use that pool?

planting flowers in it or to wash a dog

5. What is one way you can reduce the amount of electricity you use?

turning out the lights when no one is in a

room

6. What is something you can recycle?

Possible answers: paper, cardboard, aluminum, glass, plastic

Science 2
Activity Manual

A. Write the letter of the correct answer.

__B__ 1. What are things in nature that God has given us to use?

      A. pollution   B. natural resources   C. erosion

__C__ 2. Which natural resource is used mainly to produce energy?

      A. trees   B. soil   C. fossil fuels

__A__ 3. Which resource is not a fossil fuel?

      A. water   B. oil   C. coal

__A__ 4. What word is used for anything that makes the air, water, or land dirty?

      A. pollution   B. natural resources   C. erosion

B. Circle *True* or *False*.

True **(False)** 5. Most water on the earth is fresh water.

(True) False 6. We should conserve our natural resources.

(True) False 7. Some natural resources can be replaced.

True **(False)** 8. Erosion moves water from one place to another.

C. Answer the questions.

9. How do the roots of trees and other plants help the soil?

   Their roots hold the soil in place and keep it from eroding.

10. What three R words remind us to help conserve our natural resources?

    reduce, reuse, and recycle

11. What are two things that you can recycle?

    Possible answers: paper, cardboard, aluminum, glass, plastic

Lesson 44; pp. 92–105
Chapter Review

Sunrise, Sunset
Student Text pages 108–9

Name _____

Follow the directions your teacher gives you.

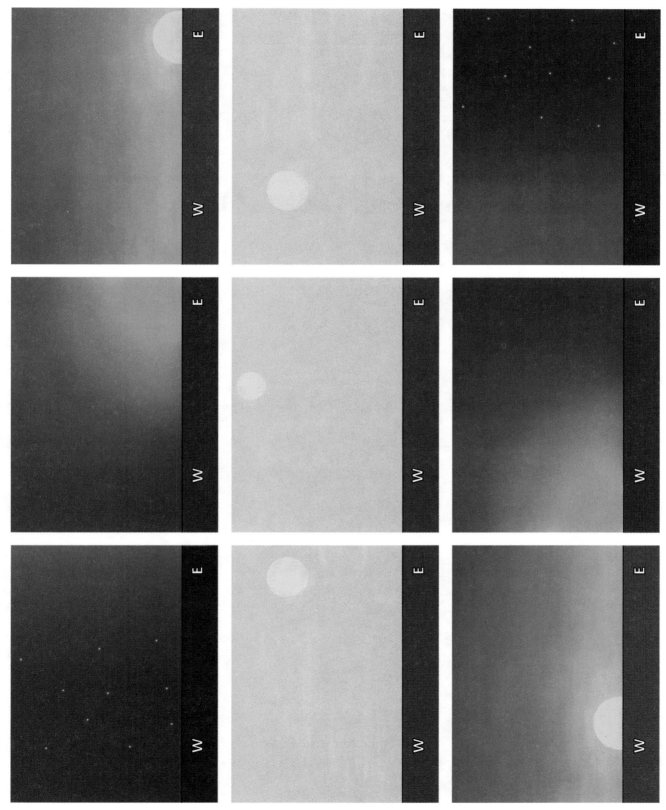

Checkup Time
Student Text pages 108–13

Name _____

Complete the puzzle.

Across

4. At sunrise, the sun appears in the _____.
6. The _____ is an imaginary line on which the earth rotates.
8. The place where the sky and the earth meet is called the _____.
9. A _____ is a model of the earth.

Down

1. The side of the earth away from the sun is having _____.
2. At sunset, the sun disappears in the _____.
3. The earth is shaped like a _____.
5. The sun is always _____.
7. Day and night happen as the earth _____.

axis	night
ball	rotates
east	shining
globe	west
horizon	

Puzzle answers:

1 Down: N I G H T
2 Down: W E S T
3 Down: B A L L
4 Across: E A S T
5 Down: S H I N I N G
6 Across: A X I S
7 Down: R O T A T E S
8 Across: H O R I Z O N
9 Across: G L O B E

Science 2 Activity Manual

Day and Night

Name _____

ACTIVITY

Purpose
Observe what causes day and night.

Materials
globe
clay (red, blue, green, and yellow)
flashlight

Procedure
A. Write where you put the red and blue pieces of clay.

1. Red: _____

_____

2. Blue: _____

B. Circle the correct answer for each marker.

3. When the light shines on the red marker…
   Red has   (daytime)   nighttime
   Blue has   daytime   (nighttime)

4. When the light shines on the blue marker…
   Red has   daytime   (nighttime)
   Blue has   (daytime)   nighttime

C. Write where you put the green and yellow pieces of clay.

5. Green: _____

6. Yellow: _____

D. Circle the correct answer for each marker.

7. When the light shines on the red marker…

Green has (daytime) nighttime

Yellow has daytime (nighttime)

8. When the light shines on the blue marker…

Green has daytime (nighttime)

Yellow has (daytime) nighttime

Conclusions

1. Did each marker have a daytime and a nighttime?

   yes

2. Which colors had daytime at the same time?

   red and green; blue and yellow

3. What causes daytime and nighttime?

   the rotation of the earth

Lesson 47; pp. 114–15
Activity

Name _____

A. Draw a picture for each season.

Spring

Summer

Autumn

Winter

B. Answer the question.

What causes the seasons?

the earth's orbit and tilt

Name _____

A. Fill in the blanks.

calendar	clock	day	revolves	rotates	365	24	year

1. The earth spins on its axis. It _____ *rotates* _____.

2. The earth travels around the sun. It _____ *revolves* _____ around the sun.

3. One complete trip around the sun is equal to a _____ *year* _____.

4. One complete rotation of the earth is equal to a _____ *day* _____.

5. There are _____ *24* _____ hours in a day.

6. We use a _____ *clock* _____ to show the time of day.

7. A _____ *calendar* _____ shows the parts of a year.

8. A year is about _____ *365* _____ days.

July

B. Write the letter of the correct answer.

_C_   9. The place where the earth and the sky meet is called the ____.

      A. calendar   B. axis   C. horizon

_A_   10. At sunrise the sun seems to come up at the horizon in the ____.

      A. east   B. south   C. west

_A_   11. At sunset the sun seems to go down at the horizon in the ____.

      A. west   B. north   C. east

_B_   12. The earth's ____ is an imaginary line that goes through the center of the earth from the North Pole to the South Pole.

      A. horizon   B. axis   C. orbit

C. Answer the questions.

13. What causes some parts of the earth to get more direct sunlight than other parts get?

the tilt of the earth

14. What causes the earth to have day and night?

the rotation of the earth

15. What causes the earth to have seasons?

the tilt and orbit of the earth

Science 2
Activity Manual

A. Decide which pictures show sources of light. Color them yellow.

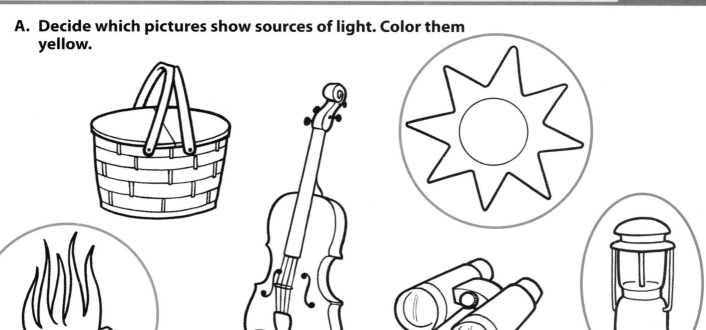

B. Draw a line that shows the path of light. Circle the object that the light is shining on.

Checkup Time

Name _____

A. Draw lines to match the first part of each sentence with the rest of the sentence.

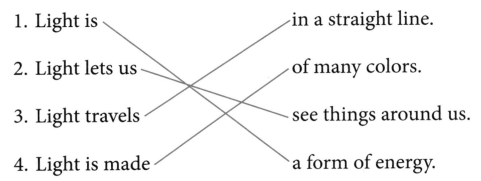

1. Light is   in a straight line.

2. Light lets us   of many colors.

3. Light travels   see things around us.

4. Light is made   a form of energy.

B. Circle the picture that answers the question.

5. Which object is NOT a source of light?

6. Which object would absorb the most light?

7. Which object would reflect the most light?

Name _____

Teaching instructions and the materials list are in the Teacher's Edition.

Test several objects. Shine the light on each object. Decide whether it is transparent, translucent, or opaque. Write the name of the object under the correct heading.

Transparent	Translucent	Opaque

Making Shadows
Student Text pages 130–31

Name _____

Cut out the lamps on the bottom of the page. Paste them in the places where they would cause the shadows to form.

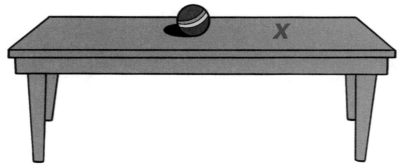

This page reinforces the concept that an object's shadow forms on the side away from the light. The student does not necessarily have to place the lamp in a certain spot as long as the lamp is on the correct side.

1.

2.

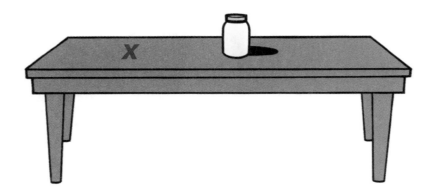

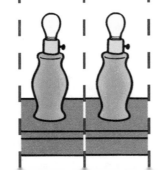

A. Circle the picture that answers the question.

1. Which object is transparent?

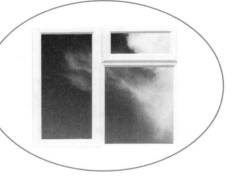  

2. Which object is opaque?

3. Which object is translucent?

B. Answer the question.

4. When does a shadow form?

when something blocks light

C. **Look at the picture. Circle the time of day you think it is.**
Explain why you think it is that time.

noon time   (late afternoon)

Why?

The dog's shadow is very large and long. Shadows are long in the late

afternoon.

How Big Is My Shadow?

Student Text pages 134–35

Purpose

Observe how your shadow changes.

Materials

sunny day
3 colors of sidewalk chalk
meter stick

Procedure

Measure your shadow. Record your measurements.

Time	Length
Morning	_____ centimeters
Noon	_____ centimeters
Afternoon	_____ centimeters

Conclusions

1. When was your shadow short?

   at noon

2. When was it long?

   in the morning and in the afternoon

3. How did the size of your shadow compare with the position of the sun in the sky?

   The shadow was long when the sun was low in the sky. It was short when the sun was high in the sky.

Lesson 56; pp. 134–35
Activity

Checkup Time
Student Text pages 120–35

Name _____

A. Write the letter of the correct answer.

__B__ 1. an object that lets some light shine through it but also blocks some of the light

__C__ 2. an object that lets all of the light shine through it

__A__ 3. an object that does not let any light shine through it

> A. opaque
> B. translucent
> C. transparent

B. Fill in the blanks.

> absorb   energy   shadow
> colors   reflect   straight line

4. Light travels in a _____*straight line*_____.

5. Light is made of many _____*colors*_____.

6. Light is a form of _____*energy*_____.

7. Light _____*reflects*_____, or bounces, off some objects.

8. Some objects _____*absorb*_____, or take in, light.

9. A _____*shadow*_____ forms when light is blocked.

C. Answer the questions.

10. What are two ways you can change a shadow?

by moving the light source or by moving the object

11. At what time of day are shadows outside the shortest?

noon

Lesson 57; pp. 120–35
Chapter Review

Science 2
Activity Manual

Cut out the pictures and phrases on page 103. Glue them in the correct boxes.

Solid

has mass
takes up space
keeps its own shape
bricks

Liquid

has mass
takes up space
changes shape to fit its container
chocolate milk

Gas

has mass
takes up space
can change its shape and size
green beach ball

can change its shape and size

takes up space

has mass

takes up space

has mass

has mass

takes up space

keeps its own shape

changes shape to fit its container

Name _____

Fill in the blanks. Use the code to help you.

A ★	G ✔	M ✪	S ▲	Y ●
B ✿	H ☺	N ✦	T ✐	Z ❋
C ✈	I ◆	O ☡	U ❀	
D ◆	J ⚓	P ☆	V ✂	
E ✿	K ▼	Q ❄	W ☆	
F ■	L ✳	R ✗	X ✛	

1. An object may change its form when it is <u>H</u> <u>E</u> <u>A</u> <u>T</u> <u>E</u> <u>D</u>
   or cooled.

2. Heating a <u>S</u> <u>O</u> <u>L</u> <u>I</u> <u>D</u> changes it to a liquid.

3. A solid <u>M</u> <u>E</u> <u>L</u> <u>T</u> <u>S</u> when it changes to a liquid.

4. Solids melt at different

   <u>T</u> <u>E</u> <u>M</u> <u>P</u> <u>E</u> <u>R</u> <u>A</u> <u>T</u> <u>U</u> <u>R</u> <u>E</u> <u>S</u>.

5. Heating a liquid changes it to a <u>G</u> <u>A</u> <u>S</u>.

6. A liquid <u>E</u> <u>V</u> <u>A</u> <u>P</u> <u>O</u> <u>R</u> <u>A</u> <u>T</u> <u>E</u> <u>S</u> when
   it becomes a gas.

7. The gas that forms from water is called water <u>V</u> <u>A</u> <u>P</u> <u>O</u> <u>R</u>.

Complete the puzzle.

Across

4. the form of matter that can change its shape and size
6. what a solid does when it changes to a liquid
7. the form of matter that keeps its shape
8. what a liquid does when it changes to a gas
9. what a liquid does when it changes to a solid

Down

1. the gas form of water
2. the form of matter that can change its shape but not its size
3. what a gas does when it changes to a liquid
5. the amount of matter in an object

condenses
evaporates
freezes
gas
liquid
mass
melts
solid
water vapor

		1 W				5 M			2 L		
3 C	4 G	A	S			M			I		
O		T				A			Q		
N	6 M	E	L	T	S			U			
D		R		7 S	O	L	I	D			
E						D					
N		V									
S		A									
8 E	V	A	P	O	R	A	T	E	S		
S		O									
	9 F	R	E	E	Z	E	S				

Purpose

Test the melting temperatures of some solids.

Materials

5 foil cups
chocolate chips
crayon
ice cube
margarine

_____

Procedure

Complete the chart.

Solid	Will It Melt?	Observations
chocolate chips		
crayon		
ice cube		
margarine		

Conclusions

1. Did any of the solids completely melt?

   yes

2. What could you do to turn any melted items back to solids?

   cool them

3. Did any of the solids not melt completely in an hour?

   yes

4. Would those solids need a higher temperature or a lower temperature in order to melt in an hour?

   a higher temperature

Lesson 61; pp. 148–49
Activity

Measuring Temperature
Student Text pages 150–51

Name _____

Instructions are in the Teacher's Edition.

Measure the temperature of each thing. Color the thermometer to show the temperature.

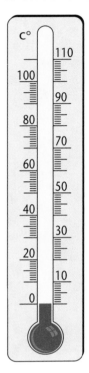

1. cup of lemonade

2. lemonade with ice cubes added

3. square of gelatin

4. gelatin after several minutes

A. Complete the matching section. Answers will be used more than once.

_____S_____ 1. has mass, takes up space, and keeps its own shape

_____G_____ 2. has mass, takes up space, and can change its size and shape

_____L_____ 3. has mass, takes up space, and takes the shape of its container

_____L_____ 4. becomes a solid when it is cooled

_____S_____ 5. becomes a liquid when it is heated

_____G_____ 6. becomes a liquid when it is cooled

G. gas
L. liquid
S. solid

B. Fill in the blanks.

condenses freezes liquid melts
evaporates gas mass solid

7. Matter can be a _____*solid*_____, a

_____*liquid*_____, or a _____*gas*_____.

8. Matter has _____*mass*_____ and takes up space.

9. A solid _____*melts*_____ when it changes to a liquid.

10. A liquid _____*evaporates*_____ when it changes to a gas.

11. A gas _____*condenses*_____ when it changes to a liquid.

12. A liquid _____*freezes*_____ when it becomes a solid.

C. Answer the questions.

13. What do we use to measure temperature?

    a thermometer

14. What gas forms when water evaporates?

    water vapor

Science 2
Activity Manual

A. Answer the questions.

1. What causes an object to move?

   a force

2. What is a force?

   a push or a pull

B. Write *push* or *pull* to describe each force.

3. _push_

4. _push_

5. _pull_

6. _pull_

7. _pull_

8. _push_

Lesson 64; pp. 154–57
Reinforcement

Science 2
Activity Manual

Observing Forces

Student Text pages 154–57

Name _____

Take a walk with your teacher. Look for things that are moving. After your walk, make a list of the forces you observed.

Circle the picture that answers the question.

1. Which pair of shoes would provide the most friction when you walk?

2. Which surface does not have very much friction?

3. Which picture shows someone adding friction to a surface?

Fill in the blanks.

direction	force	less	motion
faster	friction	more	pull

1. When something moves, it is in ___*motion*___.

2. A ___*force*___ causes something to move.

3. A force is a push or a ___*pull*___.

4. A force can change the ___*direction*___ of an object's motion.

5. A strong force makes an object go ___*faster*___ or farther.

6. ___*Friction*___ is a force that slows down or stops motion.

7. Rough surfaces cause ___*more*___ friction.

8. Smooth surfaces cause ___*less*___ friction.

Gravity

Student Text pages 160–61

Name _____

A. Look at the picture and answer the questions.

1. Are the people going up or down?

    down

2. What force is pulling them?

    gravity

    How do you know?

    Gravity pulls all things toward

    the center of the earth.

B. Answer the questions. Then use a scale to measure your weight.

3. What is weight?

    how much pull gravity has on an object

4. What do we use to measure weight?

    a scale

5. Measure gravity's pull on you. _____ pounds

Complete the puzzle.

Across

2. the number of poles a magnet has
5. the force that pulls all things toward the center of the earth
6. what opposite poles of a magnet do
8. the areas of a magnet that have the strongest magnetic force

Down

1. the force of a magnet
3. how much pull gravity has on an object
4. any object that is able to attract things made of iron
7. what like poles of a magnet do

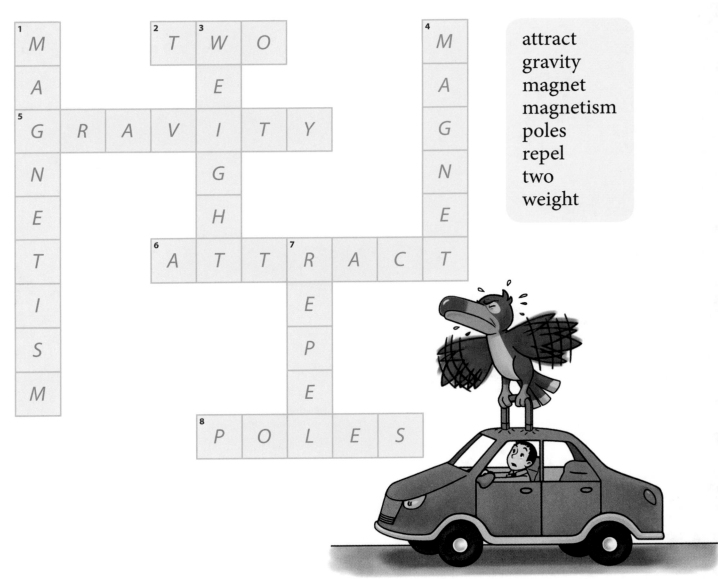

attract
gravity
magnet
magnetism
poles
repel
two
weight

Magnetic Attraction

Student Text pages 164–65

Name _____

Purpose

See which items a magnet attracts.

Materials

plastic button
eraser
nail
metal paper clip
penny
staples

_____

_____

_____

small paper bag
magnet

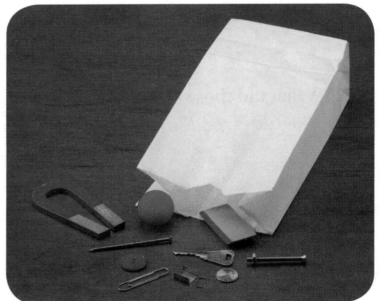

Procedure

Complete the chart.

Item	Will It Attract?	Did It Attract?
button		
eraser		
nail		
paper clip		
penny		
staples		

Conclusions

1. Which objects were attracted to the magnet?

2. What did those objects have in common?
   They were made of metal.

3. How could you classify the objects you put in the bag?
   things that are magnetic and things that are not magnetic

A. Fill in the blanks.

direction	force	pull	push	strong	weight

1. A force is a _____*push*_____ or a _____*pull*_____.

2. A _____*force*_____ causes motion.

3. A force can change the _____*direction*_____ of an object.

4. A _____*strong*_____ force can make something go faster or farther.

5. The _____*weight*_____ of an object is how much pull gravity has on that object.

B. Write the letter of the correct answer.

___*B*___ 6. the force that pulls things toward the center of the earth

___*C*___ 7. the force of a magnet

___*A*___ 8. a force that slows down or stops motion

A. friction
B. gravity
C. magnetism

C. Write *True* if the sentence is true. Write *False* if the sentence is false.

False   9. Smooth surfaces have more friction than rough surfaces.

True   10. A magnet is any object that is able to attract things made of iron.

True   11. The strongest magnetic force is found at the poles of a magnet.

False   12. Opposite poles of magnets repel each other.

Science 2
Activity Manual

Answer the questions.

1. What are the hard parts of your body that form your skeleton?

   the bones

2. What are two jobs that bones have?

   give support to the body and protect soft parts inside the body

3. What is the name of the set of bones that goes down your back?

   the spine

4. Which set of bones protects your heart?

   the ribs / the rib cage

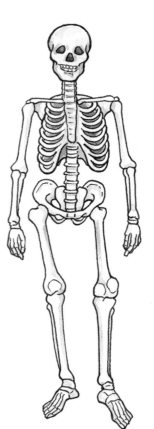

5. What are the parts of your body that work with your bones to help you move?

   the muscles

6. What is a muscle in your body that works all the time?

   Possible answer: the heart

Complete the puzzle.

Across

3. the system that includes your heart and blood vessels

5. the muscle that pumps blood through your body

6. what your lungs do when you breathe in

7. the size of your heart

8. the part of your body that helps you breathe in oxygen

Down

1. a muscle that helps air move in and out of your lungs

2. tiny tubes that move blood to all parts of your body

4. what carries oxygen and nutrients from your lungs to the rest of your body

blood
blood vessels
circulatory
diaphragm
expand
fist
heart
lungs

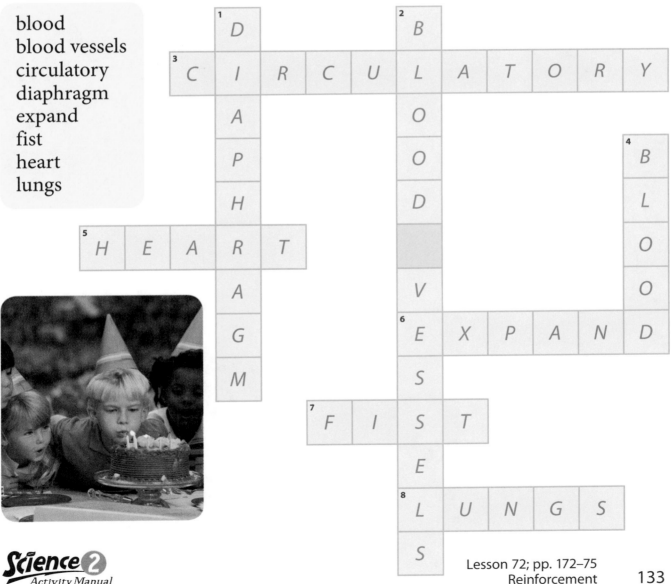

Across:
3. CIRCULATORY
5. HEART
6. EXPAND
7. FIST
8. LUNGS

Down:
1. DIAPHRAGM
2. BLOOD
4. BLOOD

Checkup Time

Student Text pages 168–75

Name _____

A. Write the letter of the correct answer.

_A_ 1. form your skeleton

_D_ 2. move your body

_B_ 3. pumps blood

_C_ 4. help you breathe

A. bones
B. heart
C. lungs
D. muscles

B. Complete the chart.

blood vessels   bones   heart   lungs   muscles

Skeletal System	Muscular System
bones	muscles

Circulatory System	Respiratory System
blood vessels heart	lungs

C. Answer the questions.

5. What are two jobs that bones have?

   give support to the body and protect soft parts inside the body

6. What part of your body is about the same size as your heart?

   your fist

7. How does oxygen get from the lungs to the rest of the body?

   The heart pumps blood to the lungs, and blood carries the

   oxygen to the rest of the body.

Activity Manual

Being Healthy
Student Text pages 176–79

Name _____

Eating the right kinds of food is important. Food can be divided into different groups. Cut out the pictures on page 139. Paste them in the correct groups.

Grains/Breads	Dairy/Milk Products	Fruits	Vegetables	Meats
bread crackers pasta	cheese milk yogurt	apple grapes pear	broccoli carrots corn lettuce	ham turkey

Activity Manual

Complete the web.

| blood vessels | heart | lungs | muscles |
| bones | intestines | mouth | stomach |

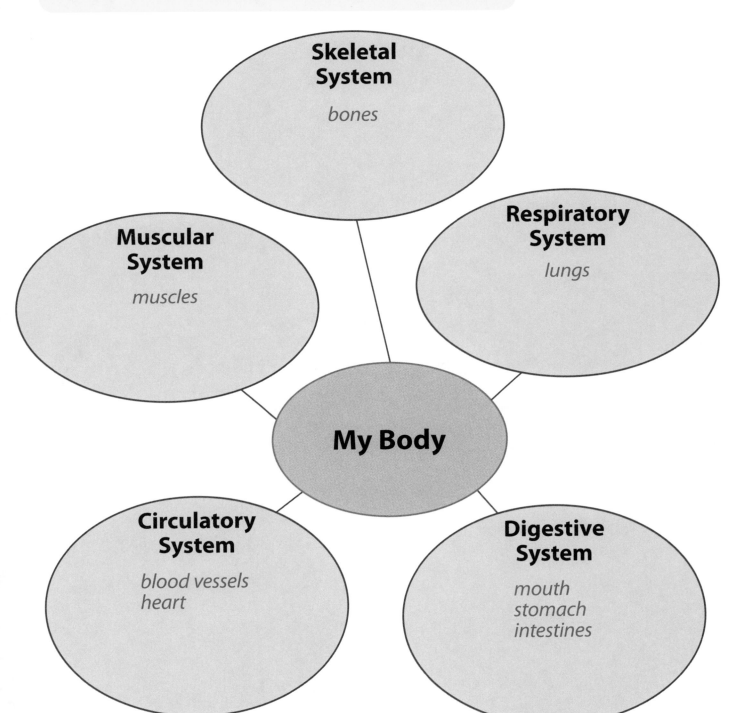

Skeletal System

bones

Respiratory System

lungs

Muscular System

muscles

My Body

Circulatory System

blood vessels
heart

Digestive System

mouth
stomach
intestines

Checkup Time

Name _____

A. Write the letter of the correct answer.

___B___ 1. The parts of your body that work together to do a job make up _____.

   A. saliva   B. a system   C. blood

___A___ 2. The muscle that pumps blood is the _____.

   A. heart   B. lungs   C. diaphragm

___A___ 3. The hard parts of your body that form your skeleton are the _____.

   A. bones   B. blood   C. intestines

___C___ 4. The part of your body that helps you take in oxygen is the _____.

   A. bones   B. stomach   C. lungs

___C___ 5. Your _____ work with your bones to help you move.

   A. lungs   B. intestines   C. muscles

___B___ 6. Your body starts to break down food in your _____.

   A. stomach   B. mouth   C. intestines

___A___ 7. Your _____ is a bag of muscle that turns food into a thick liquid.

   A. stomach   B. mouth   C. saliva

B. Number the parts to show the path of digestion in order.

___2___ 8. stomach

___4___ 9. large intestine

___1___ 10. mouth

___3___ 11. small intestine

C. Answer the questions.

12. How does the oxygen you breathe in get from your lungs to the rest of your body?

   The heart pumps blood to the lungs, and blood carries the oxygen to

   the rest of the body.

13. What are two jobs of your bones?

   to give support and to protect soft parts inside the body

14. What are two things you can do to help yourself be strong and healthy?

   exercise and eat the right kinds of foods

Photograph Credits

The following agencies and individuals have furnished materials to meet the photographic needs of this textbook. We wish to express our gratitude to them for their important contribution.

Alamy
COREL Corporation
Fotolia
Getty Images

iStockphoto.com
JupiterImages Corporation
Miriam Mitchem
123 Royalty Free

PhotoDisc, Inc.
Slip-X Solutions
United States Air Force (USAF)
Unusual Films

Wikimedia Commons
Wikipedia

Chapter 1
© 2009 JupiterImages Corporation 3 (all); © iStockphoto.com/MarsBars 5 (hand lens); PhotoDisc, Inc. 5 (ruler); Unusual Films 5 (balance), 7; © Cultura/Alamy 5 (measuring cup); © iStockphoto.com/Syldavia 5 (thermometer); © iStockphoto.com/jake020 9 (top); © iStockphoto.com/Solphoto 9 (center); Getty Images/Tetra images RF 9 (bottom)

Chapter 2
Unusual Films 13; © iStockphoto.com/Snowleopard1 15 (tiger cub); © iStockphoto.com/Nikontiger 15 (tiger); © 2009 JupiterImages Corporation 15 (seedling, frog), 23 (bottom left), 24 (top, bottom right); Daderot/Wikipedia 15 (tree); © iStockphoto.com/shevvers 15 (tadpole); © iStockphoto.com/orava 15 (colt); © iStockphoto.com/Abramova_Kseniya 15 (horse); © iStockphoto.com/UTurnPix 23 (top left); pioregur © Fotolia 23 (top right); Martin Ruegner/Digital Vision/Getty Images 23 (bottom right); National Geographic/Getty Images 24 (center left); © iStockphoto.com/AttaBoyLuther 24 (center right); Miriam Mitchem 24 (bottom left)

Chapter 3
© 2009 JupiterImages Corporation 25 (top, bottom), 31 (apple, apple tree, coconut, coconut tree, both dandelions, peach, acorns, sunflower); © iStockphoto.com/hermanc 25 (center); Unusual Films 27; © iStockphoto.com/cgbaldauf 29; Andrzej Włodarczyk © Fotolia 31 (peach tree); Indigo © Fotolia 31 (oak tree); Kaldari/Wikimedia Commons 31 (sunflower seeds)

Chapter 4
© 2009 JupiterImages Corporation 39 (left, right), 42 (monkey, tortoise), 46 (cactus, duck, monkey, fish); © iStockphoto.com/Richard Gunion 39 (center); Jon R Peters © Fotolia 42 (desert); © iStockphoto.com/Octavio Campos 42 (rainforest); © iStockphoto.com/AVTG 42 (forest); © iStockphoto.com/RyersonClark 42 (tundra), 45 (tundra); COREL Corporation 42 (deer), 46 (deer);

© iStockphoto.com/DmitryND 42 (fox), 46 (fox); Unusual Films 43

Chapter 5
© iStockphoto.com/Snowshill 51; © iStockphoto.com/digital94086 52

Chapter 6
© 2009 JupiterImages Corporation 57; Unusual Films 63; Infinite XX © Fotolia 66

Chapter 7
© 2009 JupiterImages Corporation 67, 73 (center, bottom), 75; © iStockphoto.com/nojustice 73 (top)

Chapter 8
© 2009 JupiterImages Corporation 79; Unusual Films 81

Chapter 9
© iStockphoto.com/standby 95 (top left); Marty Kropp © Fotolia 95 (top center, center center, center right, bottom left, bottom center, bottom right), 100; © 2009 JupiterImages Corporation 95 (top right); © iStockphoto.com/csheezio 95 (center left); Unusual Films 97

Chapter 10
© 2009 JupiterImages Corporation 103 (top, bottom), 105; Eric Gevaert © Fotolia 103 (center); Unusual Films 109; Chris Elwell/123RF.com 113

Chapter 11
© iStockphoto.com/christophriddle 115 (top); © 2009 JupiterImages Corporation 115 (center, bottom), 116 (bottom), 119 (top left, top right, center left, center right), 121, 130; © iStockphoto.com/Jim Green 116 (top); icholakov © Fotolia 116 (center); Slip-X Solutions 119 (bottom left); © iStockphoto.com/Vadim Ponomarenko 119 (bottom right); DoD/SSGT Jeffrey A. Wolfe / USAF 123; Unusual Films 127, 129

Chapter 12
© 2009 JupiterImages Corporation 133, 136, 144